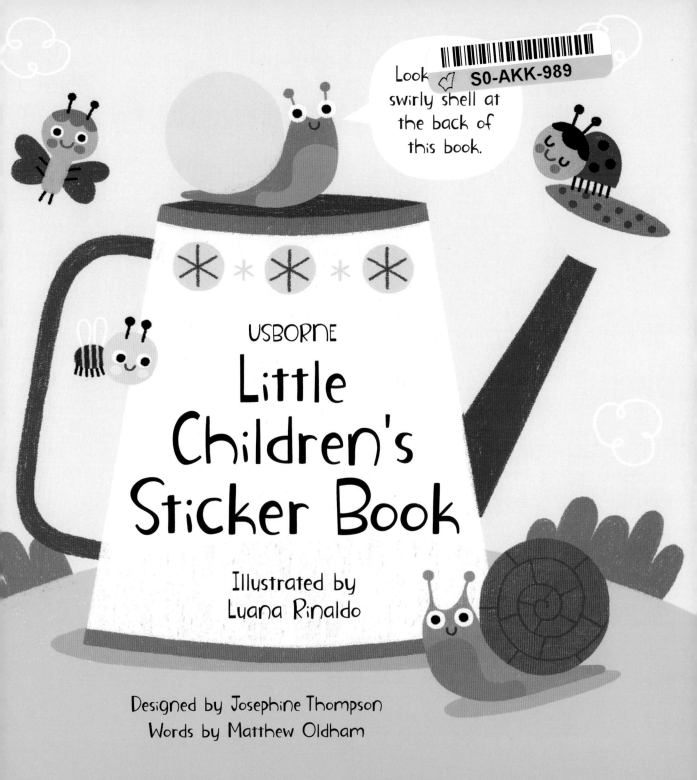

Look swirly shell at the back of this book.

SO-AKK-989

USBORNE

Little Children's Sticker Book

Illustrated by
Luana Rinaldo

Designed by Josephine Thompson
Words by Matthew Oldham

Find some raindrop stickers, please.

2

3

Buzz buzz
BUZZ...

These stems
need some
flowers.

BEEP
BEEP

6

We're going on a trip!

8

Who lives next door?

9

11

12

13

Look at those big balloons.

14

Up, up and AWAY!

16

Let's set sail into the big blue sea.

19

Brr! Dress Koala in warm winter clothes.

21

23